Mia Lofthouse
Alabaster Wilkinson
& Oz Hardwick
(ed.)

Confessions

Indigo Dreams Publishing

First Edition: Confessions
First published in Great Britain in 2022 by:
Indigo Dreams Publishing
24, Forest Houses
Cookworthy Moor
Halwill
Beaworthy
Devon
EX21 5UU

www.indigodreamspublishing.com

ISBN 978-1-912876-73-0

British Library Cataloguing in Publication Data. A CIP record for this book can be obtained from the British Library.

Designed and typeset in Palatino Linotype by Indigo Dreams.
Cover design by Alabaster Wilkinson.
Printed and bound in Great Britain by 4edge Ltd.

Papers used by Indigo Dreams are recyclable products made from wood grown in sustainable forests following the guidance of the Forest Stewardship Council.

In memory of Rosemary Mitchell,
who coined the name 'Wordspace'.

CONTENTS

Confessions

Foreword

Confessions ... we always knew from the initial idea that this theme would bring some interesting works, and we were not disappointed. What was pleasantly surprising, however, was the wide variety of prose and poetry that was sent our way. Many pieces were reflective: looking back to simpler times of childhood and mischief, a world that can seem so far away from our own in 2022. Other submissions focused more on love and the loss of it, and these pulled at our heartstrings, while other tales of misdemeanour and revenge had us both shocked and amused in equal measure.

Although we received a diverse range of submissions, there were many threads that connected the pieces together. We felt, above all, these confessions were doorways (or perhaps windows) into other people's lives. A way for us to connect with each other, to see each other more clearly, and isn't that one of the most beautiful things about writing? That you can share a part of yourself with the world. In this sense, the act of writing, whether it be prose or poetry, long-form or short, is to confess. It is to lay a part of yourself bare on the page, and I think this is why the theme seemed so promising to us during those initial days of planning this book.

In the words of Ernest Hemingway, "There is nothing to writing, all you do is sit down at a typewriter and bleed." To write is to give, to read is to receive what the writer has given and to maybe learn something in the process. We hope these confessions take you on a journey and show you a little of what it means to be human on this strange little rock.

Mia Lofthouse

Confession – Tonnie Richmond

I don't remember what you did to make me mad,
just the deep fury as I stomped homeward
on my little eight-year-old legs.

I must have planned it all in that short march
down the street from your house to mine,
my anger undiminished.

Down the long garden, into Dad's shed,
I grabbed the garden fork (as big as me)
and stormed back to your place.

I do remember thrusting, lunging at you,
but then there's a gap; later, your mother
screaming at mine, showing her the bruise

just below your eye. I'm sorry, Bill.
I'm glad I didn't poke your eye out.

You really were my second-best friend.

Crouch End – Simon Tindale

Each time I look
into the mirror
the crouching man
is getting nearer

each time I look
he's one step closer
until his hand
is on my shoulder

each time I look
the eyes are meaner
the nails are longer
the cuts are deeper

each time I look
the blade is keener
just when it flashes
the mirror smashes.

I'm Guilty – Nick Toczek

You say my shortcomings will drive you insane.
You label me idle and useless and vain.
Okay! I confess. You're dead right to complain.

I did burn that building. I brought down that plane.
I laced your dog's pet food with grade-A cocaine.
I made all those phone calls to Saddam Hussein.
And planted that microchip deep in your brain.

I've been such a pest, such a pig, such a pain.
I'm plainly the reason you're prone to migraine.
I know that I've got your respect to regain.

I co-founded UKIP. I bankrolled Sinn Fein.
I helped anti-vaxxers to run their campaign
And I advised Putin to invade Ukraine.
But please don't keep claiming that I'm inhumane.

I'm going to be nicer. Please let me explain.
Innocence will be my new-found terrain.
I'll never do nastiness ever again.

A Sick Confession – Paul Coleman

I'm twelve and I'm a sick boy: sick in cars, sick on buses, sick during the school coach trip to The Imperial War Museum.

It's still dark when we start. Somewhere in the suburbs of nineteen seventy-six my gorge rises. All there is to use is the clear plastic bag holding my sandwiches.

Instant relief.

My naked cheese sandwiches sit in my lap. Fascinated – or numb – I hold the violated see-through plastic up to the window. As the road sweeps by, I examine the finer details of my former discomfort. The noise of my schoolmates retching calls our collective plight to the attention of those in charge. The coach driver pulls over at the entrance to a leafy estate. Mr George the History teacher tells me to "find a bin" and "get rid of the thing. Pronto!" He can't look at me or the bag but only gesture vaguely at the outskirts of London. The door clatters open. Before I lurch out into the thin, crisp air, I hand him my cheese sandwiches. He can't look at them either.

I'm out of the coach in a strange land in the dawn light. I'm scared the traumatised coach party will drive off without me.

Find a bin. Find a bin.

I stumble 'round the corner to be confronted with a row of identical houses. Little lawns. Creosote lathered on fences. No bin. The smell of dew-damp grass joins the increasingly acrid odour of what's sloshing in the bag. No one is about. All the milk bottles are still on doorsteps. Not just milk but other deliveries. The coach driver pips the horn twice. Desperately, I scan the little street again for any receptacle. Tears are forming. Then I see three bottles of milk outside a door in a little plastic crate made for four.

When I get back to the rattling, petrol-reeking coach, Mr George asks me cheerfully if I found a bin alright. "Yes," I lie, "there was one just around the corner." He gives me back my sandwiches, which he has wrapped in some brown paper.

Motoring down the decades in my mind I can see, with the

pin-sharp clarity of invention, the puzzled expression on the face of a nineteen-seventy-six mum in a floral dressing gown as she regards the plastic bag with the knot in it amongst the gold tops. The children gather to see. Did we ask for soup? Please, please, please let her not have opened it.

A Panacea for the Apocalypse – Oz Hardwick

When I reassess my position – that *long, hard look* advocated by self-appointed arbiters of all things pure and mutual – I discover myself in the wrong skin and all its concomitant displacements. Exhibit A: I am in a room full of glove puppets with stitched-on wide-eyed innocence and arms open to most possibilities, my mouth full of words that prevent me from telling the truth. There are certain expectations from all concerned, but I suspect that mine are somewhat different to the clowns, bears, and crocodiles ranked in rows before me. Exhibit B: When I check my phone it is anything but a phone. Sometimes it is a block of ice with an unused theatre ticket frozen inside, sometimes it is a book of discontinued savings stamps. On very rare occasions it is a lingering scent which I have been trying to describe since I first picked up a pencil. Exhibit C: The name on my office door has very little to do with me other than certain formal similarities of curve and line. The same may be said of photographs, fingerprints, and speech inflections. The same may be said of the years I've scraped into this too-tight skin – which I maybe put on in a flustered rush after that first occasion on which I fell apart in a red, red room full of clowns, bears, and crocodiles, though I can't for the life or death of me remember – to present the illusion of time. A glove puppet raises a wise brow but the hand inside is a child's, waiting to be led somewhere safe.

Bitch – Hannah-Freya Blake

I think I've found my teeth, just now –
right here, behind my smile:
they've been bricked up in silence for so long,
I'm as hungry as a crocodile!
Venom sits thick upon my tongue,
drips like golden honey…

Come, kiss these bloody lips of mine!
I promise there's no need to worry;
I only want a little taste –
a tiny little slice –
since there's only one small part of you
that can sate my appetite.

No, not that – don't be silly!
I've no need of your…brains.

I want to eat the words you hurl me,
the words with which you aim to strike
and bruise these apple cheeks of mine
to break my jaws and bite.

I think I'll eat your throat right out,
blood and bone and all –
tongue tartar, with a jugular jou,
garnished with your spinal cord,
sour as aged revenge served cold,
sweet as rotten candy –
pleasantly accompanied by
a nice bottle of chianti.

James 5.16 – Jack Bassham

What does it mean to confess?
A declaration of triumph for some,
taking credit for sins collected over a lifetime
like marbles.
For others the lifting of shame and the release of guilt.
An all too easy escape.
Some see it as a spotlight,
the grabbers of headlines and
the faces of true crime documentaries.
Now and then one may confess out of a sense of morality,
possibly the rarest confession of them all.
Others have smaller sins to confess,
though these are often more stubbornly drawn out.
Their roots run deep throughout the years,
till lying becomes a way of life.
Some confess to the dead who may tell no tales,
graveyards are littered with the secrets of the living.
Others whisper in the ears of priests,
hoping that God may overhear.
And some secrets are uttered only to oneself in the depth of the night,
with only the burning stars to bear witness.
I do not deserve a confession of my own,
for that would free the demons imprisoned within me.
The plague of the past for which there can be no cure.
I deserve this, condemned to slowly decay.
Permanently punished for my crimes,
I am my own judge, jury and executioner.
You shall have no confession from me.

Murder Your Darlings – Jeff Cottrill

"Murder your darlings." This is the advice that many writing teachers give you. It's an old standard: if you like the scene, or the line, or the paragraph, but removing it would improve the whole, then cut it. No matter how good it is, CUT IT. Murder your darlings. The best editing advice you can get.

I always murder my darlings. That's how dedicated I am. I love my darlings, I love them with the intensity of a devoted parent, with the passion of a young newlywed. I hate to murder them, but murder them I must, for the good of the whole.

The first time is always the hardest. You struggle with the raging guilt and the pounding heartbreak. You say, "What a lovely darling this is. How can I bring myself to destroy such a beautiful thing? What madness is this? Dear God in Heaven, what am I doing?" But you know the job must be done. And you do it, but hesitantly, carelessly, sloppily. And then the time comes once again, and you dread it. You dread it as you do the euthanasia of an adorable puppy dog stricken with the plague. But it's easier the second time. And it gets even easier after that. And you get into the practice, into the habit, and you even look forward to the rush it brings. It becomes an inexplicable urge, an unquenchable addiction, to murder your darlings.

In writing, I mean.

Over the years, I've developed a special routine, all my own, of murdering my darlings. I don't like to get it over with quickly. Sure, they say, your darlings are just as dead after you do it the fast way as they are after the *laboured* way. But the fast way doesn't suit me. It's too simple, too *impersonal*. Murdering your darlings should be an artform. It should be something planned, thought through, and greedily relished. See, I don't murder my darlings right away. I like to torture them first. I lean over and I whisper, with the delicacy of a sensitive lover, "Darling. Forgive me, but you've been naughty. And now the time has come to punish you for it. What shall it be, darling? Would you care to taste the sting of jagged steel slowly sawing through your flesh? Or smell the burning of your skin as I apply red-hot irons? Or what about the slow, wrenching pain that poison brings as it plays havoc with your insides? Tell me. Tell me, and I shall deliver it like the Angel of Agony." From there, nothing can keep me from my mission – not the guilt, not the screams, not the begging, not even the bargaining. And as they suffer, I laugh and laugh and regret nothing. I extinguish the last of their hope that I may reconsider, that I may turn back, as I make my final preparations to murder my darlings.

In writing. This is all an extended metaphor, of course.

Before I commit the deed, I take one last look into their eyes, and as they whimper, as they moan, as they beg me to spare them, I say, "Shhhhhhh. Darling. The time has come. Do you believe in God? Do you believe in Heaven, or Hell, or just eternal Limbo? Wherever you believe you're going, it's time to prepare. Time to pack your bags and drop the kids off with your neighbours. Time to check in your luggage and get your passport scanned and obtain the boarding pass. Time to walk through the metal detector. Time to sit in the gate lounge, kill time by reading a book, maybe browse the magazine shop for a while, buy a glass of wine at the bar, maybe two, use the restroom one last time..."

Where was I going with this?

And where are *you* all going? Come back here, I've not finished my seminar! I still have yet to discuss the best choice of weapons and what mop to use to clean up th– oh, *great*. Here come the security fellows, as always. Why, tell me, *why* do I always get banned from these literary festivals? Huh. Damned Millennial snowflakes, always getting triggered by the slightest... humph.

Well, at least I still have my darlings. And when I get home tonight, my darlings will pay twofold. I look forward to the slashing and the burning and the beautiful damage to be done. With enough cruelty and sadism, I suppose I could... trim my novel by another fifty pages. Maybe even sixty! Seventy-five! Let's tear and rend those darlings into oblivion.

Peter – Mike Farren

I didn't call him. This seemed reasonable:
he never called me. No matter how needy
he grew, the understanding always was

that I'd call him and he'd tell me about
how he was coping in the days, weeks, months
after the girlfriend he never expected to find

left; about his shitty dead-end job;
about the classical record obsession
he couldn't afford; about his illness.

It seemed reasonable one day, when
we hadn't spoken for a couple of weeks
not to call him. The living room telephone –

it was landlines in those days – was inscrutable:
I couldn't tell if it was being reproachful
or channelling his passive aggression.

I turned my back. It gradually gave up.
This was almost twenty years ago.
I wonder how he's doing.

Forgiveness – Mia Lofthouse

Sometimes I want to set myself on fire,
just to stop the itch.

I know
that you understand how it feels
to hate your own skin: Disgust
is a familiar word to us both.
So when you pass me the gun,
and sink to your knees,
I will not ask, *why?*

I have spent half my lifetime
tending to these bullet wounds.
Bind, repeat, bind, repeat, bind,
repeat. But still, on bad days, they bleed.
I will not inflict that hurt on you.

So stand up. Don't look at me
like that. I don't need your apology
to feel whole.
I'm still angry,
I am scared,
but I would want no one to feel how I have felt,
to know each shadow by name.
Not even you.

Especially not you.

The Song of Simeon – Clint Wastling

You will know I am gay from the men I paint,
how I fix their beauty without restraint.
Two men cannot love without fear of arrest
Amoris Sacramentum is my sexuality confessed.
Six weeks detainment for attempted sodomy,
admitted to asylums to re-find my purity.
Neither worked – discharged unimproved.
At my family's insistence I was removed
to Paris, where I found my pencil true
could shade my love and mute its colours too.
Code such meanings in my painted works
then hire Henri for lust's ecstatic jerks.

Three months I lingered in a Parisian jail.
Close friends deserted – refused my bail:
Swinburne and Rossetti walked away.
Hollyer and Stenbock helped to pay
for food and lodgings, a small studio
where I might conquer in provincial shows.
In life, my rule was not to compromise
on who I am or whom I loved and never to use disguise.

I Must Tell You about Mary – Richard Wilcocks

My dearest Violet,

I have something to confess, darling, about another woman before you became my fiancée. Although I could not do it face to face without reddening, I feel able to tell you in a letter about what lingers in my head. It was a dream, one now fading. I am hoping you will be amused rather than dismayed.

It began in the Headingley Picture House, the one across the Otley Road from the grounds. I had often sat in the audience watching the flicks, and I was there just days before the surgeons had their big go at me. It was like being in front of a sort of mirror on the world, but a weird one without us in it, with an old man tinkling at a piano. I laughed myself half-barmy as that Charlie Chaplin bumbled his way through a restaurant on roller skates, and I gasped out loud at Tom Mix's stunts on horseback. We all needed to laugh. Desperately.

I am still messed up, thanks to shrapnel. The rules in the war hospital at Beckett Park are strict but it is still 1917. There's no leaving without a permit, we must endure those blue-flannel uniforms and so-called intimacy with the nurses is not allowed as well you know. Didn't that old bag matron nag you to bits? Mam comes when she can, the girls from the clothing factories still turn up in gaggles with flowers and tobacco and privates in the medical corps sing to us dressed as pierrots, white greasepaint on their faces, but for me it is the flicks every time.

On the day before my appointment with the operating table, it was all "Good afternoon for the flicks today" from my bunch of pals, but it's always a good afternoon, because it's free for the wounded at the matinée if they are wearing the blue uniform. Permits were no problem and we were soon walking past St Chad's, me hobbling, with plenty of noisy banter. Inside, it stank of cig smoke, made worse as we lit up when the curtains opened. And there she was, the famous Hollywood star Mary Pickford!

In her film, she plays Radha, an English girl abandoned in India by her father, a British Army officer addicted to drugs. Opium. You were the nurse who told me about morphine which comes from that. She is brought up by a not very dark native sword-maker who looks more Italian than Indian, and becomes a Hindu. In an uprising, she saves the life of a British captain who of course marries her when her English origins are revealed and after she has arrived in England to claim her inheritance. She drops the Hindu thing, I believe.

And the dream? Well, I never sleep easy, my mind swilling with horrors, but Mary Pickford smiled back that night at my upturned face and stepped out of the screen to be with me, then arrived on my ward as a volunteer nurse, and we paid shall we say special attention to each other. I called her "Miss Pickford" to avoid suspicion and very soon we were giggling and cuddling, including under the blankets, hands busy, and she told me she loved me even though I am not the same young man I was last year. You know what I am telling you, darling?

When I was wheeled through the ward to the operating room, the lads in their beds joshing that I was off to the flicks again, where curtains are drawn and darkness falls suddenly, I was so anxious when I smelt the ether and saw the mask descending. A hand clenched mine reassuringly, and I knew it was Mary's, but when my eyes flickered open after the slicing and sewing I saw her silently mouthing that she was not for me, that distance must be kept, as she turned and faded away out of this blighted world.

The world brightened a little when they told me I was not eligible for the artificial limb race in the summer but a lot when you walked into the ward and became engaged to me, a sentimental fool with one good and one gammy leg. I know you have a medical interest in eugenics, but I really am sane, and whole where it matters. Are you amused, Violet my love?

I remain your ever-loving sweetheart,
Charlie

In The Garden – Kathryn Roe

I haven't told you this before, I'm sure.
That hairy face that I adore is liable to leave me sore,
when in my lady garden you explore.
I hear sometimes the sad lament from labia all squashed and bent,
their silky sheen long dried and spent,
crying from beneath the spikes, "No more, dear God, no more!"
Through the fauna wild and free or neatly trimmed up topiary,
I beg you not to stomp or chomp or tread too heavily.
Pleasure can be most evasive, met with visage so abrasive.
Would it be too much to ask? Is it such an arduous task
for you to do some grooming, facially?
My clitoris can twitch in fear when beardy bristles loom so near.
It's not always in ecstasy I scream.
Perhaps a gentle lapping like a cat who's just discovered
that the lid's left off a pot of clotted cream?
(Not to suggest that should a breeze blow warm and gentle
through my knees there'd be a waft of milk or cheese
or other products dairy based, no, more a hint of fairy cakes,
of angel's breath and rainclouds on the seas.)
Judging by your vague persistence, my suggestion meets resistance,
maybe there's a greater need for candour.
Here's an idea, it's just a thought. Lie here and hold your

testicles taut,

whilst I plug in my random orbital sander.

Dead or Alive – Lauren Pizzicaroli

I step, the soil slowly hardening,
slowly biting your skin, cold, to the bone,
towards your tomb, all alone. The maple leaves rustle,
rusted, slipping through my replacement bouquet,
the petals of forget-me-nots, thrown
to the wind, thrown over my shoulder like salt.
I want to place the bouquet where you rest instead.
I know I can no longer deliver them in person.

Later, I park down the street and run and
hide behind the weeping willow, weeping,
hoping to see your ghost, holding onto my flowers,
holding onto our memories that decay, change form
as we do over time. But I never see you,
never will see you, dead or alive.

I shovel dirt, wedging the steel,
squishing it like a bug beneath my boot,
deeper, harder, don't stop, deeper, harder.
Behind the gated community, unlocked by thoughts,
alone, I ask myself: "Why am I still digging?"
"What am I hoping to find?"
The past can't be brought back to the living.
I throw my shovel back in the boot, wipe the dirt
from my knees. I try to not to look back. Drive away.

I know mistakes can't be buried, and sometimes I forget that
neither were you. Yet,
it makes me feel better, to imagine that it's true.
Because your death would be easier
to face than facing the truth:
the only one that's dead is me to you.

You Think You Know Me – Rosi Gemmel

You think you know me
with my calm smile,
ready to help
and guide your step.
You think I am mature
and will follow instructions
quietly, before disappearing
into my corner.
You think I have lived my life
and should let others live theirs
whilst shrivelling on an easy chair.
You think I can be duped
as maybe my faculties
have started to depart
on their own long journey.
You think I am useless.
But that is not counting
how I feel like a teenager
(until I see a strange person
in my mirror)
with the stamina that
my strong will gave me
and adrenalin holding my hand,
with the pugnacious blood
of the Incas
coursing around
my used body,
with the list of plans
that I wish to achieve
before I sleep forever.

Cats Make Me Sneeze – Sally Cooper

The following is the last known journal entry pertaining to Atticus Finkwistle Esq., formerly of Barton-on-Humber. His last known whereabouts are recorded as embarkation to the sea-faring vessel Good Truth, which is known to have set sail from Hull on 23 March, 1907. No further communications from Mr Finkwistle have been recovered or received by his surviving relative, Jenny Finkwistle, his unmarried niece who also lives in Barton-on-Humber.

22 March

I am sadly affected by a life-altering allergy to cats of all shapes and sizes.

More than half a century of living has taught me a thing or two, and so I can state without a shadow of a doubt that where you have creativity and romance there will always be cats. This is an indisputable fact; there is no room for debate on the matter. It is not possible for true art to flourish without their presence.

From feral cats who only visit when hungry, through to utterly domesticated and fussed-over felines who never leave their human's side, they are always present at the critical moment of innovation to one degree or another.

You might think "so what?" but let me tell you that this indisputable fact can have devastating results for those of us afflicted with both an innate poetic disposition and a physical aversion to the poor creatures. I am not talking about a simple dislike or distaste for the furry little monsters, but rather an auto-immune response that makes it practically impossible to share any enclosed space with the beasts for any length of time. As for stretching out a friendly hand to stroke their glorious little backs and absorb truly original inspiration, goodness no, that would result in days of discomfort and exhaustion, not to mention swollen and streaming eyes that hinder or even prevent any kind of successful creative activity.

It is only now with the passing of years that I am coming to understand that my lack of conventional success in the creative and romantic fields is, of course, entirely down to my rather inconveniently debilitating allergy to these creatures.

Previously, I had been prone to sinking into an air of despondency directed against my own not-too superficial talents and abilities as an artist, something I now realise was utterly ridiculous, particularly given my inimitable ability to shape words into beauteous prose at will and on a whim.

Given this revelation, I intend to do all I can to rid myself of this ridiculous tendency to sneeze in their presence and finally allow my true self to flourish as is my proclaimed destiny.

I have heard it said that exposure to allergens can benefit sufferers and so I have made detailed plans for an extended visit to the so-named "cat island" of Tashirojima, Japan, with an overnight stay in a wooden cabin that is also home to several of the local four-legged residents. I believe the animals are used to coming and going as they please at the property and the place sounds ideal for a test of my theory.

I leave on the morrow, intending to take supplies and writing materials for the journey and with the great hope that finally my life's grand oeuvre will be completed before this year is out.

Peppered Pig – Emma Wilkinson

A sprinkle here, a dusting there
Paprika in your underwear
If you can't keep it in your pants
I'll fill your kecks with fire ants

Sweet bell pepper will not do
maybe a scotch bonnet or two
perhaps a squirt of pepper spray
Will keep your roving eye at bay

And if I'm really full of luck
You'll come home drunk wanting to fuck
And willingly I'll seize my chance
to send you on a merry dance

As palms bejewelled with chilli pepper
Wrap around your cheating pecker
Wasted ardour turns to shock
When habanero meets your cock

Feigning horror and surprise
As tears begin to fill your eyes
I'll turn back to the stroganoff
Hoping that your dick falls off

Proud – Chloe Hanks

Would I need to stitch all of my poetry
from the cells of my own body? My own
blood, fragments and tissue? Should I expel it
from my womb, legs open and muscles
contracting, until each word tears my pale
pink flesh? Does it need to be ample and tangible;
something you can pass around, share it out?

If I named each poem after you, passing along my lineage
rather than the tales of my Gen Z sadness,
or if I invited you to the birth,
welcomed you in to watch as I scream them into being,
then would it be real enough for you to listen,
real enough that I'm not just a lull in
the conversation?

Read After Death – Mel Black

My Dear Son,

What I am about to tell you may change how you feel about me, but believe me, you will always be my son, the pride of my life. Please excuse your selfish mama for having kept the truth from you for so long, but I wanted to hurt neither you nor your father, and most of all, myself. I have carried this secret with me throughout my life, but now I want to come clean.

I became pregnant after I turned 16. Your father and I had just finished school. When I told him I was going to keep the baby he did not run away, but proposed and started working. We got married in summer, as was custom. My belly only bulged a little, so the secret was still safe for a while.

In autumn, our small and prudish village was half in exaltation and half in suspicion about my pregnancy. I could often feel the glances of people lingering on my back. They mumbled and whispered, most guessing correctly that I got pregnant before the wedding. Soon I became an outsider, and your father was fired from his new job. We barely made ends meet and my body grew weak. When I stroked my belly I was afraid to lose our child. Your father tried his best and started working in a hotel on the riverside. When I had enough strength, I sometimes helped out in the pub.

One night in winter, when our baby was just days away from being born, a mysterious hooded stranger entered the pub. Nobody spoke to him, but everyone stared. I felt sorry for him and tried to talk to him. He grumbled and whispered, asking if I could take a look in his room. My better judgement told me to say no, but when my shift ended, I knocked on his door. In his room, there was a crying baby lying in a cradle. I didn't think twice and took the baby in my arms. He stopped crying and looked at me with big curious eyes. The man smiled and asked me to sit down. He took off his hood, revealing a half-burnt face. In my shock, I almost let the baby fall, for he looked just like a ghost. The man told me a story I couldn't believe at first, but as the years went by, I realised that it must have been the truth. He said that his wife was pregnant and on the night the baby should've been born, their house was set on fire. The man was the only survivor, and kneeling before his burning house, he prayed desperately for his wife and son to be saved. A creature with wings and horns revealed itself before him. The creature promised that it would save the man's son if the man came with it, and another unborn baby would take the child's place.

In his grief, the man didn't care about the conditions and agreed to the deal, but once his son was brought to him, he couldn't stop thinking of the other child. He asked the creature to find the woman who would lose her baby, and the creature brought him to our village. The man quickly found out about me because of our neighbours' love for gossip, and he came to the pub to tell me the truth. The stranger pointed at my belly and said it was my baby who would never see the light of day. I didn't believe him, but soon I started to bleed. The man, now on his feet, began to cry, and asked for forgiveness, and even more— that I should raise his child in my baby's stead.

Once I stopped bleeding, I looked at the baby again, and all I could see was a child that needed a mother, and so I left the room with him in my arms. I was sad for a long time, unable to tell anyone about what had happened. But I claimed the baby as my son and never saw the stranger again. This baby was you, and this is how we met, Sam. Please, don't be too sad. I was glad to be your mother, and I never thought of you any different than if you were my own blood.

You are my son who was saved from the ashes.

I'm sorry you'll read this after I'm gone. Take care of yourself.

Love,
Mum

Sticky Fingers – Ella Burns Robbins

She had been a foolish little girl, trusting of wry smiles and twinkling eyes. Meeting over pints. Beneath the warmth of an ethanol chokehold, nothing that looks strange, feels it. She counts the days since the latest thing with deep red skin slugged towards her table, gunk oozing behind him, marking his territory. This one had three eyes, which stood upon prongs, poking out of his forehead. Not one of them blinked as he circled the table she perched at. Shamelessly, she swivelled her bar stool toward his direction, kicking her legs delightedly, and eyeballing back. Under the flashing red strobes set to dazzle and daze, she took the drink. Every womxn knows about his kind. He's indented in our hands, impressing deeper with each page of a love story that's turned. Anyone recognises his shadow from roles in romantic films, following girls out of the cinema. She knew him too, she was sure, and swore that he was trustworthy. But remembers only blackness after that.

Days later she comes to, vomiting yellow into the bathroom sink. This happens more frequently recently. Each time, she wonders how she made it back alive. If this is even living.

Over the weeks that follow, a sickly goo sludges out of her fingertips. No matter how hard she scrubs, no matter how much bleach she dilutes, or doesn't,

residue remains.

Transient – Edwin Stockdale

Corfe Castle, 1328

Edward's daily pilgrimage to the beach
between tidemark and watermark.
Each day his imprints, the traces
of his boundary, washed over,
infilled with brined water.

Behind him, the castle around a hilltop
of chalk, porous and permeable.
The castle, his dwelling place,
Purbeck limestone, pockmarked
by windows, arches and portals.

He skims six scallop shells into the Channel
for his lovers, naming them:
Gaveston, Isabella, Eleanor, Audley, Damory, Despenser.
The curve of the shells sink
under the watching of Neptune's greenroom.

Instructions – Rebecca Whittaker

Read this carefully, twice at least, then follow the instructions exactly. Go into the bedroom, find the key (you know which one) then go back downstairs. Go into the dining room and put the key in the lock. Walk to the back door, take the shed key off the hook, and go outside. Breathe deeply (you need a reminder every now and then) then go to the shed. Turn the key in the lock, push open the door, go inside and close it behind you. Take three paces forward, two steps left and crouch down. Tap the floorboard – the one with the knot – and listen until it sounds hollow. Push the hollow section and pull out the box. You know what's inside. You know what it is. I've hidden it for all these years. Forgive me.

The 6am Cabby – Lucy Wright

As the sky melted into the pastel colours of morning, headlights marched along city roads in their military formations. The humming of traffic and the bustling of the Northern line were melodic contrasts to the city clock as it called the 6am alarm. A sign of the times as the church bell chimed for morning prayers. The steeple sang its hymn as people walked in sin across the street. Taxi drivers, still tired from Sunday sabbatical shifts, would later fail to confess to their wives the four bacon butties they would eat before supper. Flocks of birds migrated across the skyline, now a watercolour image of the day before. Greasy-spoon ladies crooned as they set out metallic chairs and blackboards, breaking through the dreary moans of drunkards heading home. Girls hobbled in a murmuration with heels in their hands and pizza shop chips tangled in loosened curls. Their breath smelling of half-price student doubles, lips lined with kisses from men who had wished to take them home. The men who confessed, over text, they never fancied the half-cut girl with the half-price drinks. Later she will confess to the chemist she forgot to take her pill, and she will keep her lips closed when her mother calls, curious for stories of the night before. A gaggle of girls who forgot the names of songs that played on old fashioned juke boxes or from playlists at pre-drink parties. Tunes that filled the club with melancholy memories of other nights out. Names of bars they couldn't recall, where they sang along in gibberish to tunes they claimed to have *definitely* heard before. The morning after told a different story; karaoke lyrics searched on google, misspelled titles they didn't quite remember. Moaning and groaning with hangovers, their mouths hanging open after hearing the semi-sober confessions of the sins committed during the early hours.

The taxi rank swelled with the regular drivers, chevrons and black cabs rolling down their windows, shouting sober recitations of the names the drunks gave, but quickly forgot themselves, as fares mounted up for the boys and girls who had fallen from their silver spoons for a cheap booze-up in the local Wetherspoon. They stood on curbs, counting 50p pieces, brushing tobacco from their last £5 note while a friend vomited in Mummy's brushed leather Prada handbag. Admissions of guilt slipped from whisky-whet lips and echoed in the back seat as the cabby asked perfidious postgraduates if their "girlfriend is waiting at home?" All while the local clown lifted his mask and watched those same whisky lips kiss someone else. Secrets unravelled in small talk like a psychologist's couch as ribboned tongues untied confessions to strangers in front seats.

Inhibitions loosened. Secrets spilled. All to someone's dad on his night shift.

Each night he is exposed to the jaded vowels and consonants he expects to hear in one form or another, but it is never the same story twice. He has heard every wrongly worded sentence said to the wrong person. Every word the culprit's partner told him she wouldn't be mad if he just told her. There is never a *sorry*, just *he did this* and *she did that.*

Confronted for a confession, his passengers spill those words from serpentine tongues, breaking the weight that lies upon self-proclaimed innocent shoulders. Telling someone they don't love them anymore; there's someone else; something along those lines. The confession breaks their victim's heart into a thousand pieces. The story they had planned is overwritten. The collateral tears them from future to past to present. All the unwelcomed heartbreak because of the human delusion that we "deserve" truth, no matter the outcome. Blushed and teary-eyed, truth becomes an airborne surrendering. A story.

Turning left to divert the journey, the driver takes this one the long way home. Not for the fare, but to hear more of the morning's rhetoric from his customer.

He watches each confessor in his blind-spot mirror. The ones that regret their self-soothing lies are his favourites. The ones that know a lie is always a lie in whatever form it takes. To lie for the good of others; to confess, to admit to those secrets they hide close to their chest. The cabby savours them all. The sober ones; the drunk ones. The ironic ones from fraudsters. The ones with questionable ethics others condoned. Confessions brim with contradictions. All as the clock chimes 6am.

And it will repeat again tomorrow.

Coming Clean – Briony Molloy

We all have our secrets, some more harmful than others. My name is James, and my little secret may have caused the end of the world.

I had dreams of becoming a therapist, but I wanted to learn more about comforting people. I always admired the ease religion provided, so I decided to volunteer at the village church to learn from the local priest, Father Abe. He took me in as a cleaner, allowing me to observe his calming ways between my duties of dusting the pews, mopping the floors, and polishing the pillars.

Father Abe started spreading the gospel in the town centre every Friday at 3:30, leaving me to look after the church. Things were quiet for a while, until one week, as I was refreshing the confessional booth, I met *him*.

Tap, tap.

I jump at the knocking on the confessional door.

"Uh, mister priest, sir? I mean, Father, is that you in there?" a timid voice says. I attempt to protest, only getting one syllable out before he darts into the other booth.

"ForgivemeFatherforIhavesinned," he utters in one clumsy phrase. I'm about to object again but something stops me. This is my chance to practice what I've learned. I may not have the exact qualifications to provide salvation for this man, but God probably isn't real anyway, so what's the harm if he believes his sins are forgiven?

I take a deep breath and try to remember what Father Abe taught me about confessions. "Um…" I clear my throat and deepen my voice, "when was the last time you confessed?"

"Never."

"Alright, go ahead."

"I've been having dreams, Father."

"Having dreams is not a sin…"

"They've led to thoughts, evil thoughts." He pauses, his breath shaking. "Thoughts of violence, greed, blasphemy. I'm

- 41 -

sorry."

There's a moment of silence before I realise that he's finished... I never learnt what comes next, so, I recite a rushed, and probably incorrect, version of *The Lord's Prayer*, ending with a simple "now go in peace."

"Thank you, Father."

Nailed it.

"If I need to confess again, can I come back?" he asks.

Fear floods me. What if Father Abe finds out? He'd probably be mad... but how can I say no to this man? Besides, he seems better already.

"Sure," I splutter. How often is this guy going to come in anyway?

***

He came every week. Thank goodness I told him to return during Father Abe's preaching sessions.

It was fascinating to listen to the man's tales of crimes, lies, and wrongdoings. I found myself believing in the power of religion as I watched his confidence grow with every visit. It was miraculous, I felt like a real therapist.

But all good things must come to an end. After a few more weeks, he announced his final visit. He said the path of God wasn't right for him anymore, but as a courtesy, he wanted to thank me and confess to a final sin of "planning to help the beast out of the sea," whatever that meant.

It's now Monday afternoon and I'm considering asking Father Abe about it. Maybe he can put my mind at ease, or maybe my secret will be exposed...

"Is everything ok, boy? You can't empty the donation box by staring at it." Father Abe's voice snaps me out of my thoughts. "Not practicing witchcraft, are we?"

I crack a fake smile. "I'm fine, Father." Screw it. "Well, actually... I'm just wondering if you know what it means to 'help the beast out of the sea'?"

"Where did you hear that?" he asks, becoming suddenly stern.

"My dad," I lie, "he mentioned it last night over dinner."

His stiff posture wavers, a hellish epiphany seeping through him. He stumbles as if his knees can no longer hold the weight of his realisation. I go to ask him what's wrong, but his authoritative demeanour promptly returns. "We have to find your dad, now." He grabs my wrist, a man on a mission, dutifully dragging me with him.

"W-what? Why?"

"Your dad is the antichrist," he says hurriedly. I rip my wrist out of his grip.

"Are you out of your mind?"

Father Abe stops and looks me in the eye, explaining everything. I grow pale, guilt punching me in the gut.

That man…

His sins weren't mine to absolve. I was just making him stronger.

My lies can't continue.

"Father Abe, I need to confess… Forgive me, Father, for I have sinned."

The Journalist's Confession: What was *Really* Packed on the Blue Boat – Hannah Stone

The ebb and flow of their cities' streets
meshed into memory;
ribbons of kinship; jewelled hopes;
breath enough for prayers to Allah whose name
is blessed in cursive script
on the side of the boat;
pouches of Libyan soil sewn into pockets;
the report card of a promising fourteen year old;
the knack of getting to checkmate in three moves;
bodies in every fathom of the anchor-hold;
the small change from paying traffickers;
stones of despair;
insufficient evidence to spell out
the identities of thirty thousand
commingled remains, clattering
like scrabble pieces in the
four hundred and fifty-eight body bags
shipped in from Syracuse;
ambiguous loss.

The Unthinkable – Lucy Rice

Death blocks the view of the TV,
Glows fierce on an MRI scan,
A firefly; moving fast as lightning.

We reside, frightened, in this new land,
A map provided by Hollywood,
Ripped in fury, buried in dirt.

Time used to pass with gossip,
Tales of strange happenings;
The ghosts of Leeds, vanishing to fable.

I long for her stories now,
but they are disjointed fragments;
"I see sparrows on the lawn?" she murmurs.

In our silence we have spoken the most,
Entwining our shared DNA back to life,
I have lived the feeling of her absent laugh,

Over and over and over.
Just for a wretched moment

Against autumn's burning colours,
Children shouting, school bags clasped,
Against the backdrop of my family home,
curtains drawn

I wish for her to return. I wish for her gone.

Unrequited – Anne Caldwell

The language of now is short and full of gaps. A text message that fails to say I love you, a Facebook post without any dancing. I spend my days staring at screens, even though the lockdown has lifted and the town's full of day trippers and shoppers. I've harvested pink fur apple potatoes and washed them clean of dirt. My runner beans are blooming with red flowers and the water butts are brimming.

Today's quiet, so quiet I can hear my skin cells dividing. And I've forgotten how to hold a long conversation. It's exhausting. I'll sit and drink a glass of Chablis later on the spiral staircase and watch the sun go down. You're over the border in the Far North and my longing is bright as a cherry. Your loch will be bathed in golden evening light.

The Case of the Missing Dessert Spoons – Elend Lowry

Your old schoolfriend insisted on calling me "Sherlock" the moment I entered his house. He'd marched to war with you, brother. You hadn't returned. Your friend, however, had survived, thrived, and invited me to his wedding staged in the lovely country house that his forefathers had left him. He remembered me kindly as the quiet boy who used to do *tricks* and followed you around like I was your shadow. He'd started calling me Sherlock back then because I couldn't help but explain the trick. I wasn't amused to see the nickname had lasted a decade.

Your friend wore black, his pocket watch was on a silver chain, and the pen he'd used to seal his marriage was classically vintage. His bride was encased in white silk and her black curls cascaded down her back like midnight roses. Her bridesmaids wore a colour that sat unpleasantly between pink and yellow. I am told that these things are of import.

What I was wearing doesn't matter, save for the fact that it had an awful lot of pockets.

I drank champagne lightly during the reception. I begged off playing cards. In my silence the gamesters read that I had a run of bad luck and was cutting my losses. Smug, they left me to my circuit that briefly touched on everyone else in that grand house. I said little, smiled more often than I was used to, made sure to congratulate the lucky couple, the girl who caught the bouquet, the little lad who had carried the rings to his uncle. In the early evening, only the children were impressed by my ability to pull pennies from behind ears. Later, enough champagne had been sloshed around to make my little tricks interesting for the adults too.

I swapped place settings in a blink. I changed the colour of bow ties. I did all the little wondrous and sundry things to make people used to laughing laugh even harder. Look at my hand, see how it changes petals into sculptures of swans. See not the hand that dips behind my back and pulls out the deck of cards needed for the next trick...

They still called me Sherlock, even though I only revealed my secrets to the children that eve. I don't believe in lying to children. I reveal whenever possible how the magic works. Later I saw the young bridesmaid and her partner in crime practise palming the dessert spoons.

Do you remember your friend's grotesque muscles from rowing? He used to drag me by the shoulders and throw me into the lake. You used to laugh because we were boys and at school you were only my brother when it was convenient. I was terrified. He held me outside the window of the dorms once. The ground three floors down. I'm still afraid of heights. I asked you before you went to the front if you remembered. You laughed and said that it was all in the past, why bother? And now you're dead, so you don't remember anything.

I remember.

I remember every day of it.

He doesn't. Your friend. I can tell when he looks at me that I'm just the funny boy he went to school with, who used to follow his best chum like a shadow, and always had such clever fingers. He always liked my fingers.

I hope you find what I did funny from whatever vantage point you gained. They tell me you're looking down, but we both know that your best view these days is of my ankles and the underside of my chin. Look brother, while the bride and the groom had eyes for anyone but each other...

I slipped the wedding rings from their fingers. I took her earrings. I purloined his cufflinks. I lifted that silver chain of his pocket watch, and I took back the fountain pen that your best friend had stolen from me when I was ten and had used to sign his wedding certificate. There will be chaos in the morning. I hope it makes the papers.

But if anyone asks about the dessert spoons, I can say with solemn relief, that I had absolutely nothing to do with it.

Regretfully I Ponder – Imogen Lewis

My biggest regret was the words never said.
I left it too late, took too much time,
wasted our last minutes, dawdling, tongue-tied.
I should have just said it…no, I shouldn't have lied.

The words never said hang heavy in the air;
sour on the tongue, bitter notes of despair.
I know I should have said it,
three words to *save the day*
but I couldn't form the sentence…no! Don't go.
Wait.

I regret it. There I've said it. I said what I ought.
But regret hangs heavy, the reason we fought.
We don't get a second chance, he will always know.
Always watching from the shadows, lies the seeds we – no, I –

                                                sowed.

If I could go back, maybe I would
and say the words forgotten, the words never said.

And Yet – Jaspreet Mander

Shall we listen to the lark's melody,
its liquid notes flowing one into the other,
or to the breeze gently lapping the river,
lifting the late-winter haze on her slopes,
or to the distant rumble on the sea,
stirring up leavings long forgotten?

Surely, we have moved on,
built our separate worlds the best we could,
not done badly and yet,
veering now towards the autumn of our circuits,
we remember the peach-pink of our past
whose perfume was magical,
sun-soaked days unfurling symphonies all of their own,
evening rays bathing us in undying crimson,
youthful joys fusing beat to throb,
tender futures which could have been ours
and the strange wonders of our hearts
thrumming together as one.

We knew we could take on the whole messy world,
we said we loved each other to the hilt
but the words failed and our haven foundered.
We strode towards securities, successes, insurances.

And yet the russet loam of our love
remains lush across the sward of our lives.

Journey to the Centre of Holmfirth – Joe Williams

It was Alan's idea. He'd been reading a lot of Jules Verne books, and decided he would try to dig a tunnel to the centre of the Earth. He didn't have a spade though, except for one of those plastic ones you use on the beach, so he came round to ask if I wanted to help him. He knew there was a good spade in our shed, that Mum used for her gardening. I knew she was going to be out all day and wouldn't be using it, so I got it out and took it round to Alan's place.

We decided the easiest place to start would be the rockery in Alan's back garden. The soil there was pretty soft, and there were just a few little shrubs in the way, which were easy to get rid of. Alan said it should be him that used the spade first, because he was in charge. I told him the story that Dad had told me about a man he knew who once put a spade right through his shoe and chopped the end of his foot off, but Alan said that was a load of rubbish.

After Alan had dug the first bit, we took turns with the spade. To begin with it was quite easy, but the deeper we dug, the harder it got to get the soil out of the hole. I said we should use a bucket. The one digging could fill it with soil and pass it up to the other to get rid of. Alan said that was a good idea, and went into the house to see if he could find one, but the closest thing he could come up with was a washing-up bowl, so we had to make do with that. It helped, but it would have been a lot easier with a bucket.

After a while we'd gone so deep that it was getting hard to climb back out of the hole. I said we should dig diagonally instead of straight down, so that we could climb up the slope, but Alan said that would mean we'd have to dig much further. It was 3,950 miles to the centre of the Earth, he said, probably a bit more than that because he lived on a hill, so it was already going to take ages, and it was best to take as direct a route as possible.

I said it would have been easier if we'd gone somewhere

where there was already a deep hole, like a mineshaft or a quarry. We'd have a head start then, and wouldn't have so far to go. Alan said it was a bit late to be coming up with ideas like that, and anyway we'd probably get done for trespassing or something.

When Tracy got home from work and saw what we'd done, she went absolutely mad with us. She started shouting at Alan, saying it was no way for a thirty-five-year-old man to behave, and she couldn't believe she'd married such an idiot, and why was he hanging round with the kid from down the road? I thought it was probably best if I went home then.

I didn't see much of Alan after that. I don't think he ever made it to the centre of the Earth. And I never told Mum I'd borrowed her spade.

Indigo Dreams Publishing Ltd
24, Forest Houses
Cookworthy Moor
Halwill
Beaworthy
Devon
EX21 5UU
www.indigodreamspublishing.com